Written Calculation Teacher's Guide

Hilary Koll and Steve Mills

Schofield & Sims

Published by Schofield & Sims Ltd, Dogley Mill, Fenay Bridge, Huddersfield HD8 0NQ, UK Tel 01484 607080 www.schofieldandsims.co.uk

First published in 2015. Copyright © Schofield & Sims Ltd, 2015.

Authors: Hilary Koll and Steve Mills

Hilary Koll and Steve Mills have asserted their moral rights under the Copyright, Designs and Patents Act, 1988, to be identified as the authors of this work.

British Library Cataloguing in Publication Data

A catalogue record for this book is available from the British Library.

Commissioned by **Carolyn Richardson Publishing Services (www.publiserve.co.uk)**

Design by **Ledgard Jepson Ltd**

Cover illustration by **Joe Hance (joehance.co.uk)**

Printed in the UK by **Wyndeham Gait Ltd, Grimsby, Lincolnshire**

Extracts from The National Curriculum in England for Key Stages 1–2 © Crown Copyright. Reproduced under the terms of the Open Government Licence (OGL) www.nationalarchives.gov.uk/doc/open-government-licence/open-government-licence.htm

ISBN 978 0721712789

Contents

Introduction

Schofield & Sims Written Calculation provides carefully graded practice in the aspects of written calculation that pupils need to master by the end of Key Stage 2. It equips you, the teacher, with all you need to explain, demonstrate and teach written addition, subtraction, multiplication and division. **Written Calculation** is primarily for Key Stage 2 pupils but may also be suitable for some older pupils.

The series comprises six **Pupil Books** with accompanying **Answer Books**, plus this **Teacher's Guide** and a **Teacher's Resource Book** – both of which cover the whole series. The components of the series are described below.

The questions included in each Pupil Book incorporate a range of mathematical learning objectives from the National Curriculum 2014. These questions require pupils to apply their knowledge of place value, number facts and problem solving as well as written calculation and mathematical operations. Progression through each book provides opportunities to practise these skills, further developing pupils' conceptual understanding and fluency in maths.

Purpose and benefits

Written Calculation provides simple instruction, worked examples and structured practice in all four of the key mathematical operations. It is designed for regular classroom use alongside your existing maths lessons. As pupils progress through Key Stage 2, gradually developing their maths skills, they are also likely to change teachers on an annual basis. This series provides stability and continuity, ensuring that none of the vital steps are missed as pupils learn to apply their skills while moving up through the school. For this reason, you may wish to use **Written Calculation** as the basis of a whole-school approach to written calculation.

Further benefits of using **Written Calculation** on a regular basis include:

- preparation and good practice for national tests
- support for work in other areas of the primary and secondary curriculum
- preparation for using written calculation proficiently on a day-to-day basis in future education, in the workplace and in everyday life.

Components

Pupil Books

The six **Written Calculation** Pupil Books cover the following topics:

- **Addition**
- **Multiplication 1**
- **Division 1**
- **Subtraction**
- **Multiplication 2**
- **Division 2**

Each Pupil Book includes a simple introduction for pupils, which clearly explains the purpose of the book and how it is to be used. This introduction supports your own instructions for pupils as they begin work on each book. It is also useful for parents to refer to if you decide to set sections of the books as homework.

To guide the learner towards full mastery of the method, each Pupil Book covers 18 small 'steps' and devotes a double-page spread to each one. For each step, the method is described in detail with a full worked example followed by practice and problem solving questions, which together ensure that pupils become fully proficient in every aspect of the method. The *Summary of the steps* pages in this Teacher's Guide enable you to view at a glance the content of each Pupil Book.

Three *Check-up tests* and a *Final test* are also included in each Pupil Book. These tests help you to assess progress and monitor pupils' proficiency with the steps. To allow comparison of results, a *percentage conversion chart* is provided at the bottom of each test to allow simple conversion of scores.

The answers to all the questions in each of the six Pupil Books should be written directly into the book. Each completed Pupil Book then provides a permanent record of the pupil's work and encourages each pupil to take pride in his or her work.

Answer Books

There are six books of answers, each presented as a correctly completed Pupil Book to make marking quick and simple. Its card cover makes it a durable resource that is suitable for frequent reference and it has a useful introduction reminding you of key points. At the back of each book of answers is a photocopiable *Group record sheet* which may be used to record pupil progress for an entire class or set on this topic.

Teacher's Guide

This Teacher's Guide helps you to integrate the series within a whole-school approach to written calculation. The lesson planning and teaching notes give detailed explanations of each step for each written method.

In addition, a set of photocopiable *Assessment resources* is provided in the back of this book. Two *Assessment tests* per topic cover the same areas as the work provided in the Pupil Books (one question per step). These may be given periodically to determine how well pupils are mastering each written method. You can use them as you wish – as formal assessments, as extra practice in class or as homework activities, as pupils reach the final stages of a book. Finally, a *Mixed calculations test* gives pupils practice in deciding which operation to use for a variety of different word problems. Answers for all the resources are provided. Percentage scores from each of these can be recorded on the downloadable *Group record sheet*, available from the Schofield & Sims website. The *Group record sheet* is also included as a photocopiable resource in the back of each Answer Book.

Teacher's Resource Book

A separate Teacher's Resource Book provides photocopiable resources to supplement the material contained in each Pupil Book. These resources may be used for further practice or homework and answers are provided. The resources are all photocopiable and pupils will need spare squared paper for working.

Further practice questions provide up to ten questions per step, corresponding to the steps in the Pupil Books. Each page comprises questions covering two steps: you may wish to photocopy the whole page for pupils to work through or you may prefer to use the dotted lines and cut out the questions that correspond to a specific step in order to stick them into an exercise or homework book.

Problem solving questions provide additional word problems, similar to those appearing in the *Problem solving* section of each step in the Pupil Books.

Free downloads

Further resources are available for download from the **Written Calculation** pages of the Schofield & Sims website. These resources include, for example, lists of number bonds, a multiplication square and division facts, which some pupils may need to support their earliest steps in **Written Calculation**. The selection of downloads available is updated regularly to meet your changing requirements and the demands of the National Curriculum.

Written Calculation and the National Curriculum 2014

The Pupil Books may be used flexibly, according to your own preferences and to fit in with your school's approach to maths teaching. For example, you may wish to use certain books to support specific key points only. However, the best possible results will be obtained if pupils work systematically through the 18 steps in each Pupil Book, progressing towards mastery of each written method. It is recommended that you start with the **Addition** and **Subtraction** Pupil Books in Year 3, focusing on the early steps in these books before introducing the early steps from the other **Written Calculation** Pupil Books. You, as the teacher, will know best when to introduce each Pupil Book and how to provide a differentiated learning experience for your class that matches individual needs and targets.

Learning objectives, aligning to the National Curriculum 2014, are outlined in the *Teaching notes* within each *Planning* section of this Teacher's Guide. Where appropriate, specific learning objectives are identified within the corresponding step of the *Teaching notes*. These objectives relate to the requirements of the National Curriculum 2014. All learning objectives appear in green text and thus act as a guide to when each step of **Written Calculation** may be introduced.

A comparison of the methods used with those exemplified in the National Curriculum 2014 Mathematics Appendix 1

A range of different methods of written calculation may be used for all four operations. The methods used throughout **Written Calculation** are in line with those recommended by the National Curriculum 2014. A comparison of the methods to those exemplified in the National Curriculum 2014 is provided as a free download from the Schofield & Sims website and is also described briefly below with examples taken from the National Curriculum 2014 Mathematics Appendix 1.

Addition

The method used for addition in **Written Calculation** is exactly as demonstrated in the National Curriculum. The position of any carried digits may vary in different methods, but in **Written Calculation** they are placed below the answer. This matches the position in which they are shown in the National Curriculum Mathematics Appendix 1 and in this example.

	7	8	9
+	6	4	2
1	4	3	1
		1	1

Subtraction

Subtraction in **Written Calculation** is taught using the method known as 'decomposition'. This method has been taught widely in recent decades. This matches the first two subtraction examples given in the National Curriculum Mathematics Appendix 1.

The 'equal additions' method (that is, the third subtraction example in the National Curriculum Mathematics Appendix 1) is not used in **Written Calculation**.

	8	12	
	9	3	¹2
−	4	5	7
	4	7	5

Short multiplication

The short multiplication method is used in **Written Calculation** for one-digit multiplication only. When a number has to be multiplied by a two-digit number, pupils are taught to use long multiplication. The method of short multiplication exactly follows the method shown in the National Curriculum Mathematics Appendix I (first example).

Long multiplication

The only difference between the method of long multiplication shown in **Written Calculation** and that which is demonstrated in the third example in the National Curriculum Mathematics Appendix I is in the position of the carried digits resulting from the multiplications. In **Written Calculation** (and in the example here) they are written as small digits beside in the column to the left.

Short division

In **Written Calculation**, the short division method is used for dividing by one-digit numbers only. When a number has to be divided by a two-digit number, pupils are taught to use long division. The short division method used in **Written Calculation** exactly follows that shown in the first two examples in the National Curriculum Mathematics Appendix I.

Long division

The method for teaching long division in **Written Calculation** is as shown in the third example in the National Curriculum Mathematics Appendix I. This method is used for giving answers with remainders, as fractions and as decimals. Teaching pupils to treat all long division questions in the same way, using this more traditional approach, provides consistency of language and method.

How to use Written Calculation

Working through a step with your class

Introduction and focus

Some pupils may be able to read and follow the explanation and worked example in the *What to do* section by themselves or with a partner. However, the material is much more effective if you use it as the basis for a whole-class or group demonstration, where you model exactly what is required. The following points may be useful if you decide to take this approach:

- Draw pupils' attention to the full title of the step which helps you to focus on the specific learning point. Later you may want to comment on ways in which this step is similar to, or different from, other steps that you have worked through.

- Read the description of the step and look at the question used in the worked example. Encourage pupils to make an estimate of what they think the answer might be. You can discuss rounding at this stage and record an appropriate estimate.

What to do

- Read aloud and work through each of the points in turn under the heading *What to do*. Invite pupils to describe the process in their own words and discuss any areas of potential difficulty. Introduce relevant links to place value and expanded methods. More details for each step are given in the *Teaching notes* presented in this Teacher's Guide for the relevant Pupil Book.

Now you try

- Next ask pupils to look at the first guided example in the *Now you try* section. These questions are set out on grids, as if on squared paper, with the calculation correctly placed on the grid. Talk about how to do the calculation and encourage pupils to finish the calculation and to find the answer.

Key learning point or focus of the step

Description of the step

Explanation and worked example

Guided questions

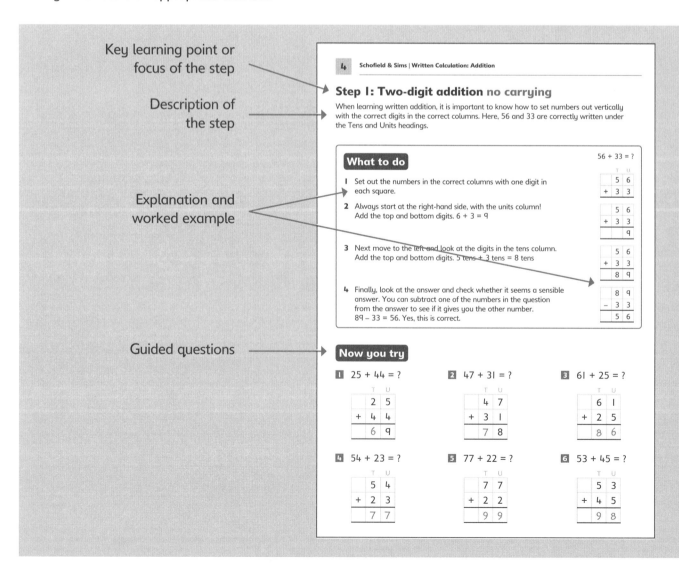

- As you work through these and all other questions, it is helpful if you stress the vital importance of **estimating and checking**. You should also make sure that pupils make the necessary **links between written methods of calculation** and **place value** Further details on both of these points are given on page 10.

- Those pupils who are confident that they can now tackle this step may work through the rest of the *Now you try* questions independently. Support those pupils who are less confident by continuing to work through the guided questions together.

More practice

- These questions provide further practice, moving pupils on to slightly different or more difficult examples of the questions covered in *Now you try*.

- In some cases the questions have not been set out on the grids. Instead pupils need to complete the grids themselves in order to gain practice in positioning correctly the numbers from the questions and then carrying out the calculation.

Problem solving

- This section contains word problems, giving pupils the opportunity to practise using written calculation in everyday contexts.

- Pupils may need extra paper for their workings out, so ensure some spare squared paper is available.

Self-evaluation

- Ask pupils to fill in the simple self-evaluation rating after they have completed all the questions in the step. Encourage them to give an honest answer. Explain that, if they feel they need extra support, this will be given.

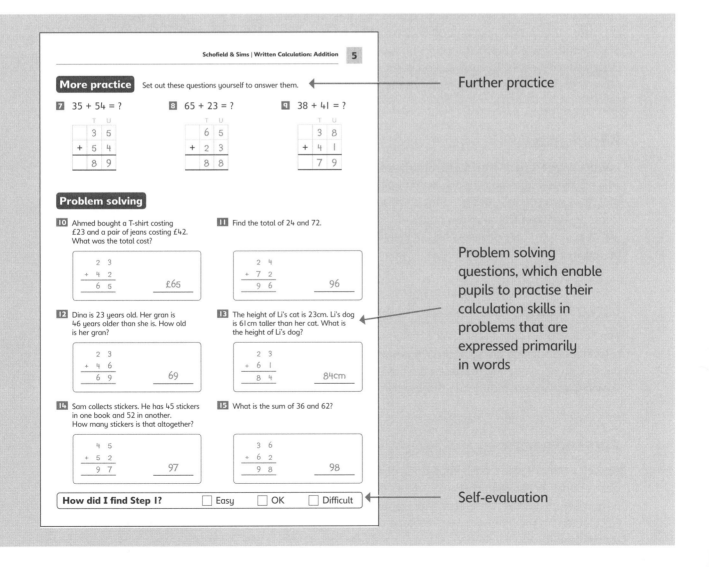

Further practice

Problem solving questions, which enable pupils to practise their calculation skills in problems that are expressed primarily in words

Self-evaluation

Prerequisites for working on Written Calculation

Pupils who have not yet memorised number bonds may find it useful temporarily to refer to a list of number bonds, which are downloadable from the **Written Calculation** pages of the Schofield & Sims website. This will allow them to focus on the procedures of the written method. Once pupils are familiar with these facts, they will no longer need the list.

Where an operation is covered by two books, as is the case for multiplication and division, pupils should work through the first book before beginning the second. Prerequisites specific to individual books are given in the *Teaching notes*.

Each of the six Pupil Books provides pupils with 18 'steps' of learning. Pupils should work through the steps consecutively to ensure they master key ideas.

The importance of estimating and checking

It is essential to remind pupils of the importance of checking their answers to see if they are sensible. As they progress, ask pupils to check each answer with an inverse calculation: for example, check a written subtraction with a written addition calculation. As pupils' confidence in a written method grows, encourage them instead to make estimates before they begin each calculation.

Linking written methods of calculation and place value

The steps in **Written Calculation** demonstrate to pupils the process of written column methods and provide them with the necessary structured practice. In order to derive the maximum benefit, it is important that pupils have a good understanding of place value. You can enhance pupils' understanding of why and how each process works by drawing links between the methods they are learning and place value concepts. In each section of this Teacher's Guide, key *Teaching notes* and expanded representations of the written methods are given to support you.

Marking

Correct answers to all the questions and tests in the Pupil Books are provided in the book of answers, which is available to accompany each Pupil Book. You can enter pupils' results on the *Group record sheet* that has been specially designed for each book and is available in the back of each Answer Book or from the **Written Calculation** pages of the Schofield & Sims website. Recording the results in this way will help you to track progress and to identify any weak areas where a recap on particular steps may be required.

Extension

The final steps in each Pupil Book extend more able pupils and address more difficult aspects of written calculation, including giving decimal answers. They may be used at your discretion to stretch those pupils who have already mastered the basics. Corresponding *Further practice questions* and *Problem solving questions* are included in the Teacher's Resource Book.

Assessment

As well as the 18 steps, each Pupil Book also contains three *Check-up tests* and a *Final test* to help assess pupils' progress in particular areas. These may be used exactly as you wish, either in class or as homework. Correct answers are presented in the books of answers so that a total score can be calculated and then the simple *percentage conversion chart* found at the bottom of each test can be used if desired.

Addition:
planning

Addition: planning

Learning objectives

The **Addition** Pupil Book leads pupils through the necessary steps for mastering the traditional column method of addition. This method involves setting out digits vertically in columns, adding the digits in each column from right to left and, where a total of more than 9 is made, 'carrying' a digit to the column to its left. The carried number is placed below the answer.

Th	H	T	U
3	9	2	8
+ 3	5	6	7
7	4	9	5
	1		1

The steps in the **Addition** Pupil Book address the following learning objectives from the National Curriculum.

Step National Curriculum: Addition

Year 3

1
- Recognise the place value of each digit in a three-digit number
- Read and write numbers up to 1000 in numerals and in words

2
- Add and subtract numbers with up to three digits, using formal written methods of columnar addition and subtraction

3
- Estimate the answer to a calculation and use inverse operations to check answers

4
- Solve problems, including missing number problems, using number facts, place value and more complex addition and subtraction

5

6 **Year 4**
- Recognise the place value of each digit in a four-digit number

7
- Add and subtract numbers with up to four digits using the formal written methods of columnar addition and subtraction where appropriate

8
- Solve addition and subtraction two-step problems in context, deciding which operations and methods to use and why

9

10

11 **Year 5**
- Use rounding to check answers to calculations and determine, in the context of a problem, levels of accuracy

12
- Add and subtract whole numbers with more than four digits, including using formal written methods (columnar addition and subtraction)

13

14 **Year 6**
- Read, write, order and compare numbers up to 10 000 000 and determine the value of each digit

15

16
- Use estimation to check answers to calculations and determine, in the context of a problem, an appropriate degree of accuracy

17

18 Beyond Year 6 for more able extension

Summary of the steps

Written Calculation: Addition

Step 1	**Two-digit addition** no carrying
Step 2	**Three-digit addition** no carrying
Step 3	**Three-digit addition** carrying 1 ten
Step 4	**Three-digit addition** carrying 1 hundred
Step 5	**Three-digit addition** carrying once, including answers greater than 999
Step 6	**Three-digit addition of three numbers** carrying once

Check-up test 1	**Two- and three-digit addition, including carrying once**

Step 7	**Four-digit addition** carrying once
Step 8	**Three-digit addition** carrying twice
Step 9	**Four-digit addition** carrying once or twice
Step 10	**Three- and four-digit addition** carrying once or twice, answers greater than 9999
Step 11	**Four-digit addition** carrying three times
Step 12	**Addition of three numbers with three and four digits** carrying up to three times

Check-up test 2	**Three- and four-digit addition, with up to three carries**

Step 13	**Five-digit addition** carrying up to four times
Step 14	**Addition of a list of numbers**
Step 15	**Large number addition**

Check-up test 3	**Addition of large numbers**

Step 16	**Decimal addition** one decimal place
Step 17	**Decimal addition** two decimal places
Step 18	**Decimal addition** different numbers of decimal places

Final test	**Addition of whole numbers and decimals**

Prerequisites

Place value

- Pupils beginning this book should understand the value of digits in two- and three-digit numbers initially. As they work through the book, they should progress to being able to identify the value of each digit in four- and five-digit numbers. The final steps in this book extend more able pupils, providing them with opportunities to add larger numbers and decimals, and here a knowledge of tenths, hundredths and thousandths is required.

Addition bonds

- Pupils should also have had sufficient experience with adding and subtracting single-digit numbers and know their addition bonds to 20: for example 7 + 8, 13 + 6. Pupils who know these facts by heart will find learning written addition much easier than those who have to work out each part of an addition.

- If any pupils have not yet memorised all their addition bonds, give them a list of number facts. Initially this will allow them to focus on the procedures of the written method and, as their knowledge of the facts grows, will enable them to master the written methods without the lists.

Teaching notes

Steps 1 and 2: Two- and three-digit addition no carrying

The first two steps introduce and familiarise pupils with setting out questions vertically on squared paper with the correct digits in each column. No carrying takes place.

- Use place value cards and partition numbers into tens and units or hundreds, tens and units to reinforce the value of the digits in each position: for example 57 = 50 + 7, 267 = 200 + 60 + 7.

- Revise column headings TU and HTU to ensure pupils understand their meanings.

Step 3: Three-digit addition carrying 1 ten

Carrying is introduced, where the two units digits have a total greater than 9.

- Explain that the 10 units are carried over to become 1 ten in the tens column.

- For pupils who struggle to understand why we need to carry, show how we could write the total of the digits in each column in an expanded form (see example, with the bold digit being carried).

	5	3	7
+	1	4	5
		1	2
		7	0
+	6	0	0
	6	8	2

Step 4: Three-digit addition carrying 1 hundred

Here carrying takes place from tens to hundreds, where the two tens digits have a total greater than 9.

- Explain that the 10 tens are carried over to become 1 hundred in the hundreds column.

- Demonstrate how we could write the total of the digits in each column in an expanded form to demonstrate why we carry (see example, with the bold digit being carried).

	4	6	3
+	2	6	4
			7
	1	2	0
+	6	0	0
	7	2	7

Step 5: Three-digit addition carrying once, including answers greater than 999

This step includes four-digit answers and carrying in either position.

- Ensure that pupils are familiar with the thousands digit in four-digit numbers. Pupils can be shown to either carry the final digit or just write it straight into the thousands column of the answer.

Step 6: Three-digit addition of three numbers carrying once

Pupils are introduced to adding more than two numbers. This is the first time they encounter a carried digit that is not simply 1.

Step 7: Four-digit addition carrying once

This step involves adding two four-digit numbers and carrying once. It is the first time pupils will carry 10 hundreds to become 1 thousand.

- Ensure that pupils are familiar with the thousands digit in four-digit numbers. No answers are greater than 9999 in this step.

Step 8: Three-digit addition carrying twice

In the context of adding two three-digit numbers, pupils will first encounter carrying twice.

- When an answer is a four-digit number, pupils can be shown to either carry the final digit or just write it straight into the thousands column of the answer.

Steps 9 and 10: Three-and four-digit addition carrying once or twice, answers greater than 9999

In these steps pupils are given the opportunity to decide for themselves whether carrying is required once or twice. Note that carrying can occur in either adjacent or non-adjacent columns.

- Where the numbers in a question have different numbers of digits, pupils can make mistakes when setting them out. Reinforce the column headings and ensure pupils place the digits correctly.

- Pupils may now be ready to focus on rounding numbers and making estimates before beginning each calculation. If they are less confident in the process of carrying, this can be postponed until they are more secure.

Step 11: Four-digit addition carrying three times

By this stage carrying should be becoming an automatic process and errors that occur are likely to be attributable to careless adding.

- Remind pupils to round numbers to make estimates before each calculation and then to use these to check their answers.

- Look for patterns in the addition errors that pupils are making: for example a pupil may frequently give an incorrect answer to 6 + 8. Give such a pupil a card with the addition bond on one side and the answer on the other for further practice.

Step 12: Addition of three numbers with three and four digits carrying up to three times

As for Step 6, this step will involve carried digits other than 1, where the totals of the digits in a column are 20 or more.

- Remind pupils to look for numbers that pair to make 10. Some pupils may also find it useful to lightly mark or cross out digits as they add them so numbers are not added more than once.

Step 13: Five-digit addition carrying up to four times

Pupils working at this step should now be confident in the process of written addition.

- Remind pupils to make estimates before calculating and then use these to check each answer.

Step 14: Addition of a list of numbers

As for Steps 6 and 12, this step will involve carried digits other than 1, where totals of the digits in a column are 20 or more. An additional focus here is on pupils setting out questions in columns for themselves.

- Remind pupils, when adding whole numbers, to line them up from the right so that all the units digits are correctly aligned first.

Step 15: Large number addition

This step extends more able pupils, showing them that the process of addition is the same for very large numbers. It provides them with the opportunity to name and use large numbers and to add them to make totals up to and beyond a million.

- Help pupils to correctly say large numbers aloud. Show how we group digits into sets of three from the right and discuss the appropriate column headings.

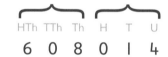

- Further place value work can be given here on reading and writing large numbers, particularly those that involve zeros: for example 608014.

Steps 16, 17 and 18: Decimal addition

The final three steps extend more able pupils by showing them that the process of addition can be used for decimals.

- Ensure pupils understand tenths, hundredths and thousandths.

- When adding decimals with different numbers of digits, pupils sometimes experience difficulty with the positioning of the digits in columns. Whereas for whole numbers all the digits line up on the right, for decimals with different numbers of digits the column headings or the decimal points must be used to ensure that they are correctly aligned.

Assessment test 1 and **Assessment test 2** at the back of this book will help you to identify the steps that each pupil has mastered, as each question number in the tests corresponds to a step.

Further practice questions for each step are given in the Teacher's Resource Book. Photocopy and cut out each section if required.

Problem solving questions, that is mixed addition word problems for the steps, are provided in the Teacher's Resource Book.

Subtraction: planning

Subtraction: planning

Learning objectives

The **Subtraction** Pupil Book leads pupils through the necessary steps for mastering the traditional column method of subtraction, sometimes known as 'decomposition'.

This method involves setting out digits vertically in columns, subtracting a digit in each column from the one above and, if the digit being subtracted is larger than the one above it, one is 'exchanged' or 'borrowed' from the column to its left and used to make the subtraction possible.

Th	H	T	U
⁵6̸	¹1	8	7
− 1	8	2	3
4	3	6	4

The steps in the **Subtraction** Pupil Book address the following learning objectives from the National Curriculum.

Step	National Curriculum: Subtraction
1	**Year 3**
2	• Recognise the place value of each digit in a three-digit number
	• Read and write numbers up to 1000 in numerals and in words
3	• Add and subtract numbers with up to three digits using formal written methods of columnar addition and subtraction
4	
	• Estimate the answer to a calculation and use inverse operations to check answers
5	
	Year 4
6	• Recognise the place value of each digit in a four-digit number
7	• Add and subtract numbers with up to four digits using the formal written methods of columnar addition and subtraction where appropriate
8	
9	**Year 5**
10	• Use rounding to check answers to calculations and determine, in the context of a problem, levels of accuracy
11	• Add and subtract whole numbers with more than four digits, including using formal written methods (columnar addition and subtraction)
12	
13	
	Year 6
14	• Solve problems involving addition, subtraction, multiplication and division
15	• Use estimation to check answers to calculations and determine, in the context of a problem, an appropriate degree of accuracy
16	• Read, write, order and compare numbers up to 10 000 000 and determine the value of each digit
17	
	Beyond Year 6 for more able extension
18	

Summary of the steps

Written Calculation: Subtraction

Step 1   **Two-digit subtraction** no exchange

Step 2   **Three-digit subtraction** no exchange

Step 3   **Three-digit subtraction** exchanging 1 ten for 10 units

Step 4   **Three-digit subtraction** exchanging 1 hundred for 10 tens

Step 5   **Three-digit subtraction** exchanging once

Check-up test 1   Two- and three-digit subtraction, including one exchange

Step 6   **Four-digit subtraction** exchanging 1 thousand for 10 hundreds

Step 7   **Four-digit subtraction** exchanging a ten and a thousand

Step 8   **Three-digit subtraction** exchanging twice, adjacent digits

Step 9   **Four-digit subtraction** exchanging twice, adjacent digits

Step 10   **Four-digit subtraction** with a zero in the column to be exchanged from

Check-up test 2   Three- and four-digit subtraction, with up to two exchanges and a zero

Step 11   **Five-digit subtraction** exchanging twice, non-adjacent digits

Step 12   **Five-digit subtraction** exchanging twice, adjacent digits

Step 13   **Five-digit subtraction** with a zero in the column to be exchanged from

Step 14   **Five-digit subtraction** exchanging three or four times

Step 15   **Five-digit subtraction** with zeros in the columns to be exchanged from

Check-up test 3   Five-digit subtraction, with several exchanges and zeros

Step 16   **Large number subtraction**

Step 17   **Decimal subtraction** two decimal places

Step 18   **Decimal subtraction** different numbers of decimal places

Final test   Subtraction of whole numbers and decimals

Prerequisites

Place value

- Pupils beginning this book should have an understanding of the value of digits in two- and three-digit numbers initially. As they work through the book, they should progress to being able to identify the value of each digit in four- and five-digit numbers. The final steps in the book extend more able pupils, providing them with opportunities to subtract larger numbers and decimals, and here a knowledge of tenths, hundredths and thousandths is required.

Subtraction bonds

- Pupils should also have had sufficient experience with adding and subtracting single-digit numbers and know their subtraction bonds to 20: for example 9 – 6, 16 – 8. Pupils who know these facts by heart will find learning written subtraction much easier than those who have to work out each part of a subtraction.

- If any pupils have not yet memorised all their subtraction bonds, give them a list of number facts. Initially this will allow them to focus on the procedures of the written method and, as their knowledge of the facts grows, will enable them to master the written methods without the lists. (A list of number bonds can be downloaded for this purpose from the **Written Calculation** pages on the Schofield & Sims website.)

Teaching notes

Steps 1 and 2: Two-digit and three-digit subtraction no exchange

The first two steps introduce and familiarise pupils with setting out questions vertically on squared paper with the correct digits in each column. No exchange takes place.

- Use place value cards and partition numbers into tens and units or hundreds, tens and units to reinforce the value of the digits in each position: for example 57 = 50 + 7, 267 = 200 + 60 + 7.

- Revise column headings TU and HTU to ensure pupils understand their meanings.

Step 3: Three-digit subtraction exchanging 1 ten for 10 units

Exchange is introduced, where the digit being subtracted in the units column is larger than the digit above it.

- Explain that we borrow 1 ten and exchange it for 10 units so that we have 10 more units to allow the subtraction to take place.

- For pupils who struggle to understand why we need to exchange, show how we could partition the first number and then move 10 across (see example).

	5	⁶7̶	¹3
–	1	4	8
	4	2	5

$573 = 500 + 70 + 3 = 500 + 60 + 13$

Step 4: Three-digit subtraction exchanging 1 hundred for 10 tens

Here exchange takes place from hundreds to tens, where the digit being subtracted in the tens column is larger than the digit above it.

- Explain that 1 hundred is being moved to become 10 tens.

- Demonstrate, again by partitioning, why we exchange in the way that we do: for example $617 = 600 + 10 + 7 = 500 + 110 + 7$.

Step 5: Three-digit subtraction exchanging once

Step 5 includes exchanging in either position.

- By this stage pupils should be starting to be able to describe the process of exchange in their own words. Encourage them to explain the process to others in the class.

Step 6: Four-digit subtraction exchanging 1 thousand for 10 hundreds

Four-digit numbers are introduced in this step.

- Ensure that pupils are familiar with the thousands digit. Discuss how a four-digit number can be partitioned to demonstrate the method here.

Step 7: Four-digit subtraction exchanging a ten and a thousand

This step involves subtracting two four-digit numbers and exchanging more than once. The digits are not adjacent, making this easier than the next two steps.

Steps 8 and 9: Three- and four-digit subtraction exchanging twice, adjacent digits

Subtracting where exchange is taking place in two adjacent columns provides a further complexity, initially with three-digit numbers (Step 8) and then with four-digit numbers (Step 9).

- When exchange occurs in adjacent columns, pupils can be shown partitioning to explain the process: for example $823 = 800 + 20 + 3 = 800 + 10 + 13 = 700 + 110 + 13$.

Step 10: Four-digit subtraction with a zero in the column to be exchanged from

An additional level of complexity occurs when a zero is the digit in a column that you need to exchange from. Exchange is therefore required twice.

- Partitioning can again be used to demonstrate the method: for example $702 = 700 + 0 + 2 = 600 + 100 + 2 = 600 + 90 + 12$.

Steps 11 and 12: Five-digit subtraction exchanging twice, non-adjacent or adjacent digits

By this stage exchanging should be becoming an automatic process and errors that occur are likely to be attributable to careless subtracting.

- Pupils may now be ready to focus on rounding numbers and making estimates before beginning each calculation. If they are less confident in the process of exchanging, this can be postponed until they are more secure.

- Look for patterns in the subtraction errors that pupils are making: for example a pupil may frequently give an incorrect answer to $13 - 8$. Give such a pupil a card with the subtraction bond on one side and the answer on the other for further practice.

Step 13: Five-digit subtraction with a zero in the column to be exchanged from

As for Step 10, this step will involve zeros in columns to be exchanged from.

- Emphasise the need to first exchange one from the column to the left of the column with the zero digit.

Step 14: Five-digit subtraction exchanging three or four times

Pupils working at this step should now be confident in the process of written subtraction.

- Remind pupils to make estimates before calculating and then use these to check each answer.

Step 15: Five-digit subtraction with zeros in the columns to be exchanged from

As for Steps 10 and 13, this step will involve zeros in the digits of the first number. Here several zeros are next to each other.

- Where pupils experience difficulties, they can be taught to use a 'counting on' method for such questions: for example pupils might count on from the smaller number up to the next multiple of 1000 or 10000 and then on to the larger number.

Step 16: Large number subtraction

This step extends more able pupils, showing them that the process of subtraction is the same for very large numbers. It provides them with the opportunity to name and use large numbers and to subtract them from one another to find differences.

- Help pupils to correctly say large numbers aloud. Show how we group digits into sets of three from the right and discuss the appropriate column headings.

- Further place value work can be given here on reading and writing large numbers, particularly those that involve zeros: for example 608014.

Steps 17 and 18: Decimal subtraction

The final two steps extend more able pupils by showing them that the process of subtraction can be used for decimals.

- Ensure that pupils understand tenths, hundredths and thousandths.

- When subtracting decimals with different numbers of digits, pupils sometimes experience difficulty with the positioning of the digits in columns. Whereas for whole numbers all the digits line up on the right, for decimals with different numbers of digits the column headings or the decimal points must be used to ensure that they are correctly aligned. Writing zeros to give decimals the same numbers of digits is important, particularly if the number being subtracted has more decimal places than the first number.

Assessment test 1 and **Assessment test 2** at the back of this book will help you to identify the steps that each pupil has mastered, as each question number in the tests corresponds to a step.

Further practice questions for each step are given in the Teacher's Resource Book. Photocopy and cut out each section if required.

Problem solving questions, that is mixed subtraction word problems for the steps, are provided in the Teacher's Resource Book.

Multiplication I:
planning

Multiplication 1: planning

Learning objectives

The **Multiplication 1** Pupil Book leads pupils through the necessary steps for mastering the traditional column method of short multiplication and begins to prepare pupils for long multiplication.

	H	T	U
	1	3	7
×			5
	6	8	5
		1	3

This method involves setting out digits vertically in columns, multiplying the digit in each column by the multiplier, from right to left and, where a total of more than 9 is made, 'carrying' a digit to the column to its left and adding it to the next product.

This short multiplication method is used in **Written Calculation** for one-digit multiplication only.

The steps in the **Multiplication 1** Pupil Book address the following learning objectives from the National Curriculum.

Step	National Curriculum: Multiplication 1
	Year 3
1	• Recognise the place value of each digit in a three-digit number
2	• Recall and use multiplication and division facts for the 3, 4 and 8 multiplication tables
3	• Write and calculate mathematical statements for multiplication and division using the multiplication tables that they know, including for two-digit numbers times one-digit numbers, using mental methods and progressing to formal written methods
4	• Solve problems, including missing number problems, involving multiplication and division, including integer scaling problems and correspondence problems in which *n* objects are connected to *m* objects
5	
6	
7	**Year 4**
8	• Multiply two-digit and three-digit numbers by a one-digit number using formal written layout
9	• Solve problems involving multiplying and adding, including using the distributive law to multiply two-digit numbers by one digit, integer scaling problems and harder correspondence problems such as *n* objects are connected to *m* objects
10	
11	• *Pupils practise to become fluent in the formal written method of short multiplication for multiplying using multi-digit numbers, and short division with exact answers when dividing by a one-digit number (non-statutory requirements)*
12	
13	**Year 5**
14	• Multiply numbers up to four digits by a one- or two-digit number using a formal written method, including long multiplication for two-digit numbers
15	• Solve problems involving addition, subtraction, multiplication and division and a combination of these, including understanding the meaning of the equals sign
16	
17	• Multiply and divide whole numbers and those involving decimals by 10, 100 and 1000
18	

Summary of the steps

Written Calculation: Multiplication I

Step 1	**Two-digit × one-digit** no carrying	
Step 2	**Two-digit × one-digit** carrying units to tens	
Step 3	**Two-digit × one-digit** carrying units to tens	
Step 4	**Three-digit × one-digit** carrying units to tens	
Step 5	**Three-digit × one-digit** carrying tens to hundreds	
Step 6	**Two-digit × one-digit** carrying tens to hundreds	
Check-up test 1	**Two- and three-digit × one-digit, with up to one carried digit**	
Step 7	**Two-digit × one-digit** carrying twice	
Step 8	**Three-digit × one-digit** carrying twice with answers less than 1000	
Step 9	**Three-digit × one-digit** carrying twice with answers greater than 1000	
Step 10	**Three-digit × one-digit** carrying twice in any position	
Step 11	**Four-digit × one-digit** with answers less than 10 000	
Check-up test 2	**Two-, three- and four-digit × one-digit, carrying twice**	
Step 12	**Four-digit × one-digit** carrying up to four times	
Step 13	**Four- and five-digit × one-digit**	
Step 14	**Six- and seven-digit × one-digit**	
Check-up test 3	**Four-, five-, six- and seven-digit × one-digit**	
Step 15	**Three-digit × 10 or × 20**	
Step 16	**Three-digit × any two-digit multiple of 10**	
Step 17	**Four- and five-digit × any two-digit multiple of 10**	
Step 18	**Three- and four-digit × a multiple of 100 or 1000**	
Final test	**Multiplying by one-digit numbers or by multiples of 10, 100 or 1000**	

Prerequisites

Place value

- Pupils beginning this book should have an understanding of the value of digits in two- and three-digit numbers initially. As they work through the book, they should progress to being able to identify the value of each digit in four- and five-digit numbers. The final steps in the book begin to prepare pupils for long multiplication by giving them experience of multiplying numbers by multiples of 10, 100 and 1000.

Multiplication tables facts

- Pupils should also have had sufficient experience with multiplying single-digit numbers together: for example 4×8, 3×2. Pupils who know all their times tables by heart will find learning written multiplication much easier than those who have to work out each part of a multiplication.

- If any pupils have not yet memorised all their tables, give them a multiplication square. Initially this will allow them to focus on the procedures of the written method and, as their knowledge of the facts grows, will enable them to master the written methods without the multiplication square. (A multiplication square can be downloaded for this purpose from the **Written Calculation** pages on the Schofield & Sims website.)

Teaching notes

Step 1: Two-digit × one-digit no carrying

This first step introduces and familiarises pupils with setting out questions vertically on squared paper with the correct digits in each column and working from right to left. No carrying takes place.

- Use place value cards and partition numbers into tens and units to reinforce the value of the digits in each position: for example $32 = 30 + 2$. Ensure pupils understand that each part is multiplied separately, starting with the units: for example 32×3 can be answered by first multiplying 2 by 3 and then 30 by 3.

- Revise column headings TU to ensure pupils understand their meanings.

Steps 2 and 3: Two-digit × one-digit carrying units to tens

Carrying is introduced, where the product of the units digit multiplied by the multiplier has a total greater than 9. Step 2 uses easier multipliers, with harder multipliers such as 6, 7, 8 and 9 used in Step 3.

- Explain that each set of 10 units can be carried over to become 1 ten in the tens column.

- For pupils who struggle to understand why we need to carry, show the expanded form of the multiplication (see example, with the bold digit being carried).

		2	7
	×		3
		2	1
		6	0
		8	1

Step 4: Three-digit × one-digit carrying units to tens

Here carrying takes place in the same way but with three-digit numbers.

- Emphasise the importance of working from right to left and multiplying each digit by the multiplier one at a time.

- Demonstrate the expanded form to explain when we carry in the short multiplication method (see example, with the bold digit being carried).

		3	2	8
×				3
			2	4
			6	0
		9	0	0
		9	8	4

Step 5: Three-digit × one-digit carrying tens to hundreds

Step 5 includes carrying where the product of the tens digit multiplied by the multiplier has a total greater than 9.

- Again the expanded method can be used to reinforce the place value of the digits in the answer (see example, with the bold digit being carried).

		1	6	2
×				3
				6
		1	8	0
+		3	0	0
		4	8	6

Step 6: Two-digit × one-digit carrying tens to hundreds

In this step pupils are reminded that, if there are no hundreds to be multiplied but there is a carried digit, this carried digit must be written into the hundreds column of the answer. Pupils will gradually learn that the carried digit can be written straight into the answer.

Steps 7 and 8: Two- and three-digit × one-digit carrying twice with answers less than 1000

These steps introduce carrying twice, where each digit multiplied produces a number greater than 9. Step 7 is for two-digit numbers and Step 8 is for three-digit numbers (answers less than 1000).

- Pupils are now beginning to become familiar with the process of carrying. Observe multiplication errors that pupils might make: for example, they may have incorrectly recalled tables facts for particular products. Give out a card with the tables question on one side and the answer on the other for further practice. Revise the more difficult tables facts to ensure that recall of the facts is quick and accurate.

Steps 9 and 10: Three-digit × one-digit carrying twice with answers greater than 1000

In these steps pupils are given the opportunity to decide for themselves whether carrying is required and in what position. Four-digit answers occur in both steps.

- Ensure pupils are confident in understanding the place value of four-digit numbers.

- Pupils may now be ready to focus on rounding numbers and making estimates before beginning each calculation. If they are less confident in the process of carrying, this can be postponed until they are more secure.

Step 11: Four-digit × one-digit with answers less than 10000

By this stage carrying should be becoming an automatic process and errors that occur are likely to be attributable to careless multiplying.

- Remind pupils to round numbers to make estimates before each calculation and then to use these to check their answers.

Step 12: Four-digit × one-digit carrying up to four times

This step involves carrying up to four times in each multiplication.

- Observe frequent careless errors made in multiplications and revise the more difficult tables facts: for example $7 \times 8 = 56$, $7 \times 7 = 49$.

Step 13: Four- and five-digit × one-digit

As the process of short multiplication becomes more automatic, pupils can begin to focus on making appropriate estimates and using these to check their answers.

- Remind pupils to make estimates before calculating and then to use these to check their answers.

Step 14: Six- and seven-digit × one-digit

This step extends more able pupils, showing them that the process of short multiplication is the same for very large numbers. It provides them with the opportunity to name and use large numbers and to multiply numbers up to and beyond a million.

- Help pupils to correctly say large numbers aloud. Show how we group digits into sets of three from the right and discuss the appropriate column headings.

- Further place value work can be given here on reading and writing large numbers, particularly those that involve zeros: for example 608 014.

Steps 15, 16 and 17: Three-, four- and five-digit × 10 or × 20 or × any two-digit multiple of 10

These steps extend more able pupils and begin to prepare them for the method of long multiplication developed in **Multiplication 2**.

- Help pupils to appreciate that when we multiply by 10 the digits of the number are moved one place to the left. Show them how multiplying by 20 can be done in two stages – multiplying by 10 and then by 2 or vice versa.

- In Steps 16 and 17 pupils can be shown that multiplying by a multiple of 10 (for example 40) has the same result as multiplying the number by 4 and then making the answer 10 times larger by moving the digits to the left one place or vice versa.

Step 18: Three- and four-digit × a multiple of 100 or 1000

In this final step pupils will be multiplying numbers by multiples of 100 and 1000 which provides further preparation for long multiplication.

- Show pupils how digits can be moved two or three places to the left to multiply numbers by 100 and 1000 respectively.

Assessment test 1 and **Assessment test 2** at the back of this book will help you to identify the steps that each pupil has mastered, as each question number in the tests corresponds to a step.

Further practice questions for each step are given in the Teacher's Resource Book. Photocopy and cut out each section if required.

Problem solving questions, that is mixed multiplication word problems for the steps, are provided in the Teacher's Resource Book.

Multiplication 2: planning

Multiplication 2: planning

Learning objectives

The **Multiplication 2** Pupil Book leads pupils on from mastering the traditional column method of short multiplication to mastering long multiplication. It also provides pupils with practice in multiplying decimals.

This method involves setting out digits vertically in columns, multiplying each digit of the first number by each digit of the multiplier in turn (giving a line for each) and then adding to find the total. Carried numbers are shown at the bottom rather than above, because this is the method most commonly taught in schools.

Th	H	T	U	
		1	1	6
	×		2	3
		3	4₁	8	← 116 × 3
+	2	3₁	2	0	← 116 × 20
	2	6	6	8

The steps in the **Multiplication 2** Pupil Book address the following learning objectives from the National Curriculum.

Step	National Curriculum: Multiplication 2
	Year 4
1	• Multiply two-digit and three-digit numbers by a one-digit number using formal written layout
2	
3	
	Year 5
4	• Multiply numbers up to four digits by a one- or two-digit number using a formal written method, including long multiplication for two-digit numbers
5	
6	• Multiply and divide whole numbers and those involving decimals by 10, 100 and 1000
7	• Solve problems involving addition, subtraction, multiplication and division and a combination of these, including understanding the meaning of the equals sign
8	• Solve problems involving multiplication and division, including scaling by simple fractions and problems involving simple rates
9	
10	
	Year 6
11	• Multiply multi-digit numbers up to four digits by a two-digit whole number using the formal written method of long multiplication
12	• Use estimation to check answers to calculations and determine, in the context of a problem, an appropriate degree of accuracy
13	
14	• Solve problems involving addition, subtraction, multiplication and division
15	• Multiply one-digit numbers with up to two decimal places by whole numbers
16	Beyond Year 6 for more able extension
17	
18	

Summary of the steps

Written Calculation: Multiplication 2

Step 1	**Three- and four-digit × one-digit**
Step 2	**Two-, three- and four-digit ×10 and ×20**
Step 3	**Two- and three-digit × a teens number** no carrying in the addition
Step 4	**Two- and three-digit × a teens number** with carrying in the addition
Step 5	**Three-digit × a teens number** five-digit answers
Check-up test 1	**Up to four-digit × one-digit, ×10, ×20 and × teen numbers**
Step 6	**Three-digit × any two-digit multiple of 10**
Step 7	**Two- and three-digit × two-digit** no carrying in the addition
Step 8	**Two- and three-digit × two-digit** with carrying in the addition
Step 9	**Three-digit × two-digit** five-digit answers
Step 10	**Four- and five-digit × two-digit**
Check-up test 2	**Up to five-digit × two-digit**
Step 11	**Three-digit × three-digit multiples of 100**
Step 12	**Three-digit × three-digit multiples of 10**
Step 13	**Multiplying two three-digit numbers** easier tables facts
Step 14	**Multiplying two three-digit numbers** harder tables facts
Check-up test 3	**Three-digit × three-digit**
Step 15	**Simple decimals × one-digit**
Step 16	**Simple decimals × two-digit**
Step 17	**Multiplying two decimals** with one decimal place
Step 18	**Multiplying two decimals** with one or two decimal places
Final test	**Long multiplication of whole numbers and decimals**

Prerequisites

Place value

● Pupils beginning this book should have already completed **Multiplication 1** and so should have an appreciation of the place value of numbers up to and beyond four-digit numbers. They should also have an understanding of the movement of digits one, two or three places to the left when multiplying by 10, 100 or 1000 respectively.

Multiplication tables facts

● Pupils should also have had sufficient experience with multiplying single-digit numbers together: for example 4 × 8, 3 × 2. Pupils who know all their times tables by heart will find learning written multiplication much easier than those who have to work out each part of a multiplication.

● If any pupils have not yet memorised all their tables, give them a multiplication square. Initially this will allow them to focus on the procedures of the written method and, as their knowledge of the facts grows, will enable them to master the written methods without the multiplication square. (A multiplication square can be downloaded for this purpose from the **Written Calculation** pages on the Schofield & Sims website.)

Teaching notes

Step 1: Three- and four-digit × one-digit

The first step revises short multiplication to ensure pupils are ready to start this book.

● Observe whether pupils are confidently multiplying using the short multiplication method, including carrying correctly and knowing their tables facts. If not, provide them with one of the assessments from **Multiplication 1** in this Teacher's Guide to see whether they need to work through all or some of the steps again.

Step 2: Two-, three- and four-digit × 10 and × 20

Here pupils are given experience of writing digits one place to the left to multiply by 10, and then multiplying by 2 as a means of multiplying by 20.

● Remind pupils that when we multiply a number by 10 its digits move one column to the left and, if a whole number is being multiplied, a zero is written in as a 'place holder' (see example). It is vital to explain to pupils why we do this, not merely tell them to write a zero into the units digit of the answer. Show how multiplying by 20 can be done in two stages, multiplying first by 10 and then by 2 or vice versa.

Step 3: Two- and three-digit × a teens number
no carrying in the addition

Long multiplication is introduced for the first time in this step in order to multiply teens numbers. The final additions are simple and do not involve carrying.

● Emphasise that the first row is the answer to the top number multiplied by the units digit of the multiplier and that the second row is the answer to the top number multiplied by 10. Discuss that this could have been done the other way round and the answer would have been the same.

Step 4: Two- and three-digit × a teens number with carrying in the addition

This step includes carrying in the addition.

- Note that the carried digits made during the short multiplication should not be counted again.

- Encourage pupils to write the addition carries using a different coloured pencil if they find it difficult to remember which carried digits to include.

Step 5: Three-digit × a teens number five-digit answers

Answers in this step go beyond 9999, but the methods used are the same.

Step 6: Three-digit × any two-digit multiple of 10

This step prepares pupils for multiplying by other two-digit numbers, greater than teens.

- Pupils can be shown that multiplying by a multiple of 10 (for example 40) has the same result as multiplying the number by 4 and making the answer 10 times larger by moving the digits to the left one place or vice versa.

Steps 7 and 8: Two- and three-digit × two-digit

In these steps pupils are given the opportunity to use long multiplication for multiplying two- or three-digit numbers by other two-digit numbers. While no carrying is required in the addition in Step 7, carrying is required in Step 8.

- Demonstrate the movement of the multiplications shown by arrows in the worked example, working from right to left in a pattern.

- In Step 8, remind pupils that the carried digits made during the short multiplication should not be counted again. Encourage pupils to write the addition carries using a different coloured pencil if they find it difficult to remember which carried digits to include.

Step 9: Three-digit × two-digit five-digit answers

As the process of long multiplication becomes more automatic, pupils can begin to focus on making appropriate estimates and using these to check their answers. By this stage carrying should be an automatic process and errors that occur are likely to be attributable to careless multiplying or adding.

- Pupils may now be ready to focus on rounding numbers and making estimates before beginning each calculation. If they are less confident in the process of carrying, this can be postponed until they are more secure.

Step 10: Four- and five-digit × two-digit

Pupils should now be confident to tackle multiplication of larger numbers in the same way.

- Remind pupils to make estimates before calculating and to use these to check their answers.

- Observe frequent careless errors made in multiplications and revise the more difficult tables facts: for example $7 \times 8 = 56$, $7 \times 7 = 49$.

Steps 11 and 12: Three-digit × three-digit multiples of 100 and 10

These steps prepare pupils for long multiplication by three-digit numbers. Step 11 explores multiples of 100, revising the place value idea of digits moving two places to the left. Step 12 involves two rows of answers that are then added together to reach the final answer to the calculation.

- Pupils can be shown that multiplying by a multiple of 100, for example 400, has the same result as multiplying the number by 4 and then making the answer 100 times larger by moving the digits to the left two places or vice versa.

Steps 13 and 14: Multiplying two three-digit numbers

More able pupils will be extended by these steps which introduce three-digit by three-digit long multiplication. Easier tables facts are used in Step 13, progressing to more difficult ones in Step 14, to give pupils more confidence in multiplying until the method is mastered.

- For less confident pupils, write what each row is the product of: for example, for the calculation 996 × 573, write 996 × 3, 996 × 70 and 996 × 500 beside the calculation.

Steps 15 and 16: Simple decimals × one- and two-digit numbers

The remaining steps, including Steps 15 and 16, extend more able pupils and involve multiplying with decimals. Steps 15 and 16 explore multiplying a whole number by a decimal.

- Help pupils to appreciate that we can compare the decimal question with a whole number question and then adjust the answer to match the original decimal question. Initially encourage pupils to make an approximation as to whether it is 10 or 100 times smaller than the whole number answer.

- Remind them how to make a number 10 or 100 times smaller by moving the digits across one or two places to the right, inserting a decimal point at the correct position (see Step 17 for more information).

Steps 17 and 18: Multiplying two decimals with one or two decimal places

Where two decimals are multiplied pupils can begin to be taught a useful check for where the position of the decimal point should be in the final answer to the calculation.

- A useful way to check if you have put the decimal point in the correct place is to count up the number of digits after the decimal points in the question and check that the same number are in the answer: for example 5.1 × 3.6 = 18.36.

- Help pupils to see this pattern but encourage them just to use this as a check initially and still to make the appropriate approximation first.

Assessment test 1 and **Assessment test 2** at the back of this book will help you to identify the steps that each pupil has mastered, as each question number in the tests corresponds to a step.

Further practice questions for each step are given in the Teacher's Resource Book. Photocopy and cut out each section if required.

Problem solving questions, that is mixed multiplication word problems for the steps, are provided in the Teacher's Resource Book.

Division I:
planning

Division 1: planning

Learning objectives

The **Division 1** Pupil Book leads pupils through the necessary steps for mastering the traditional column method of short division and begins to prepare pupils for long division.

	H	T	U
	2	4	6
4)	9	¹8	²4

Unlike the written methods for addition, subtraction and multiplication where you work from right to left, for this method pupils work from left to right. The answers are also, unusually, written above the question instead of below it.

The short division method is used for dividing by one-digit numbers only.

The steps in the **Division 1** Pupil Book address the following learning objectives from the National Curriculum.

Step	National Curriculum: Division 1
	Year 3
1	● Recall and use multiplication and division facts for the 3, 4 and 8 multiplication tables
2	● Solve problems, including missing number problems, involving multiplication and division, including integer scaling problems and correspondence problems in which
3	*n* objects are connected to *m* objects
4	**Year 4**
5	● Recall multiplication and division facts for multiplication tables up to 12 × 12
6	● *Pupils practise to become fluent in the formal written method of short multiplication for multiplying using multi-digit numbers, and short division with exact answers when dividing*
7	*by a one-digit number (non-statutory requirements)*
8	
	Year 5
9	● Divide numbers up to four digits by a one-digit number using the formal written method of short division and interpret remainders appropriately for the context
10	● Solve problems involving multiplication and division, including scaling by simple
11	fractions and problems involving simple rates
12	
	Year 6
13	● Use estimation to check answers and determine, in the context of a problem, an appropriate degree of accuracy
14	● *Pupils practise addition, subtraction, multiplication and division for larger numbers, using the formal written methods of columnar addition and subtraction, short and*
15	*long multiplication, and short and long division (non-statutory requirements)*
16	● Use written division methods in cases where the answer has up to two decimal places
17	
	Beyond Year 6 for more able extension
18	

Summary of the steps

Written Calculation: Division I

Step 1   **Two-digit ÷ one-digit** no carrying

Step 2   **Three-digit ÷ one-digit** no carrying

Step 3   **Two-digit ÷ one-digit** carrying 1 ten

Step 4   **Two-digit ÷ one-digit** carrying several tens

Step 5   **Three-digit ÷ one-digit** carrying once

Check-up test 1   **Two- and three-digit ÷ one-digit, with carrying**

Step 6   **Three-digit ÷ one-digit** first digit smaller than the divisor

Step 7   **Three-digit ÷ one-digit** carrying tens

Step 8   **Three-digit ÷ one-digit** second digit smaller than the divisor

Step 9   **Four-digit ÷ one-digit** carrying once, any position

Check-up test 2   **Three- and four-digit ÷ one-digit, carrying once**

Step 10   **Three-digit ÷ one-digit** carrying twice

Step 11   **Four-digit ÷ one-digit** carrying two or three times

Step 12   **Three- or four-digit ÷ one-digit** answers with remainders

Step 13   **Five-digit ÷ one-digit** answers with or without remainders

Check-up test 3   **Three-, four- and five-digit ÷ one-digit, carrying more than once and remainders**

Step 14   **Four-digit ÷ one-digit** with fraction remainders

Step 15   **Four-digit ÷ one-digit** with remainders as decimals, 1 dp

Step 16   **Four-digit ÷ one-digit** with remainders as decimals, 2 or 3 dp

Step 17   **Three-digit ÷ one-digit** with remainders as recurring decimals

Step 18   **Dividing decimals by one-digit numbers**

Final test   **Whole numbers or decimals ÷ one-digit, with remainders**

Prerequisites

Place value

- Pupils beginning this book should have an understanding of the value of the digits in two- and three-digit numbers initially. As they work through the book, they should progress to being able to identify the value of each digit in four- and five-digit numbers. The final steps in the book give pupils the opportunity to write remainders as fractions and as decimals. It is important that pupils know the values of the digits to the right of the decimal point for this work.

Multiplication and division facts

- Pupils should also have had sufficient experience with multiplying and dividing small numbers: for example 4×8, $32 \div 4$. Pupils who know all their times tables and related division facts by heart will find learning written division much easier than those who have to work out each part of a division.

- If any pupils have not yet memorised all their tables, give them a multiplication square to provide them with the answers to the times tables. They can use these to derive the related division facts. Initially this will allow pupils to focus on the procedures of the written method and, as their knowledge of the facts grows, will enable them to master the written methods without the multiplication square. (A multiplication square can be downloaded for this purpose from the **Written Calculation** pages on the Schofield & Sims website.)

Teaching notes

Steps 1 and 2: Two- and three-digit ÷ one-digit no carrying

These first two steps introduce and familiarise pupils with setting out questions vertically on squared paper with the correct digits in each column, working from left to right and writing answers above the question. No carrying takes place.

- Use place value cards and partition numbers into tens and units to reinforce the value of the digits in each position: for example $36 = 30 + 6$. Ensure pupils understand that each part is divided separately, starting with the tens: for example $36 \div 3$ can be answered by first dividing 30 by 3 and then 6 by 3.

Step 3: Two-digit ÷ one-digit carrying 1 ten

Carrying is introduced, where there is a remainder after dividing the tens digit by the divisor. This remainder is carried to the right and written next to the units digit (see example).

- For pupils who struggle to understand why we need to carry, the expanded or chunking method can be used to explain this process (see example).

	2	4
4)	9	¹6

	2	4	
4	9	6	
	8	0	← $20 \times 4 = 80$
	1	6	← $4 \times 4 = 16$

Step 4: Two-digit ÷ one-digit carrying several tens

Here the digit carried is more than 1.

- Emphasise the importance of working from left to right, dividing each digit by the divisor one at a time.

Step 5: Three-digit ÷ one-digit carrying once

Step 5 includes carrying from the hundreds column to the tens. The numbers used are always multiples of the divisor so there are no remainders in the answers.

- Again the expanded method can be used to reinforce the place value of the digits in the answer.
- Pupils may also need to be reminded that zero divided by a number is zero.

Step 6: Three-digit ÷ one-digit first digit smaller than the divisor

Here the first digit of the three-digit number is smaller than the divisor and so can be carried or the first two digits can be taken together.

- Discuss this process and enable pupils to gradually appreciate that it is not necessary to carry because the first two digits can be taken together and divided.
- Pupils should also start to realise that writing zero here is not necessary.

Step 7: Three-digit ÷ one-digit carrying tens

Here the first digit is a multiple of the divisor but the tens digit is not, so carrying must take place from the tens to the units.

- Pupils are now beginning to appreciate the process of carrying. Observe division errors that pupils might make: for example, they may have incorrectly recalled particular division facts. Give out a card with the question on one side and the answer on the other for further practice. Revise the more difficult division facts to ensure that recall of the facts is quick and accurate.

Step 8: Three-digit ÷ one-digit second digit smaller than the divisor

Here pupils will need to write a zero digit in the answer as the second digit is smaller than the divisor.

Step 9: Four-digit ÷ one-digit carrying once, any position

Pupils are given the opportunity to decide for themselves whether carrying is required and in what position, working with four-digit numbers.

- Ensure pupils are confident in understanding the place value of four-digit numbers and that they remember to carry any remainder to the column to the right.

Steps 10 and 11: Three- and four-digit ÷ one-digit carrying two or three times

In these stages carrying should be becoming an automatic process and errors that occur are likely to be attributable to careless dividing.

- Pupils may now be ready to focus on rounding numbers and making estimates before beginning each calculation. If they are less confident in the process of carrying, this can be postponed until they are more secure.

Step 12: Three- or four-digit ÷ one-digit answers with remainders

In this step the numbers to be divided are not multiples of the divisor, so each answer will have a remainder (r). At this stage pupils should just write the remainder as a number: for example r4.

- Remind pupils to make estimates before calculating and to use these to check their answers.

Step 13: Five-digit ÷ one-digit answers with or without remainders

Pupils should now be fluent in using the method of short division. They should be able to decide whether to carry and whether to write the answer with a remainder.

- Observe which pupils are working confidently and accurately. Look out for frequent errors caused by a division fact not recalled correctly.

Step 14: Four-digit ÷ one-digit with fraction remainders

This step extends more able pupils, showing them that remainders can be written as fractions.

- Pupils should be confident in understanding fractions and realise that, if the whole number remainder is divided by the divisor, then the denominator of the fraction will be the divisor with the numerator being the remainder. Help pupils to appreciate this by a simple pictorial example: for example 7 cakes shared between 3 people is 2 r1 but, if that 1 cake remaining is shared between the 3 people, they will each get $\frac{1}{3}$.

- Fractions may be simplified, where possible, but this is not the focus here.

Steps 15, 16 and 17: Three- and four-digit ÷ one-digit with remainders as decimals

The remaining steps extend more able pupils and continue the method of short division to give remainders as decimals. Step 15 has answers with one decimal place and Step 16 has two or three decimal places, while Step 17 explores the concept of recurring decimals.

- Help pupils to appreciate that, when we put a decimal point at the end of a whole number and write zeros after it, the number does not change in size. It is the same number. Once pupils appreciate this they can continue the process of short division and give decimal answers.

- In Step 17 pupils are introduced to recurring decimals. Explain that there are some fractions, for example $\frac{1}{3}$, which cannot be written as a finite decimal. The process of short division can begin to help pupils to appreciate why this is. Encourage pupils to put a dot over the last digit to show it is recurring and to write the answer on the line below the calculation.

Step 18: Dividing decimals by one-digit numbers

The final step shows how short division can be used to divide decimals by single-digit numbers.

- Ensure that pupils are familiar with the column headings for tenths, hundredths and thousandths.

- Explain that the decimal point in the answer must be aligned with the one in the question.

Assessment test 1 and **Assessment test 2** at the back of this book will help you to identify the steps that each pupil has mastered, as each question number in the tests corresponds to a step.

Further practice questions for each step are given in the Teacher's Resource Book. Photocopy and cut out each section if required.

Problem solving questions, that is mixed division word problems for the steps, are provided in the Teacher's Resource Book.

Division 2:
planning

Division 2: planning

Learning objectives

The **Division 2** Pupil Book leads pupils through the necessary steps for mastering the traditional column method of long division. It is vital that pupils learn the process for one-digit numbers first, although long division is used mainly for dividing by two-digit numbers or larger ones.

Unlike the written methods for addition, subtraction and multiplication where you work from right to left, for this method pupils work from left to right. The answers are also, unusually, written above the question instead of below it.

The steps in the **Division 2** Pupil Book address the following learning objectives from the National Curriculum.

Th	H	T	U
		3	1	8

$$1\ 2\ \overline{)\ 3\ 8\ 1\ 6}$$

	H	T	U
	3	8	1	6
−	3	6		
		2	1	
	−	1	2	
			9	6
		−	9	6
				0

Step	National Curriculum: Division 2
	Year 4
1	• *Pupils practise to become fluent in the formal written method of short multiplication for multiplying using multi-digit numbers, and short division with exact answers when dividing*
2	*by a one-digit number (non-statutory requirements)*
3	• Recall multiplication and division facts for multiplication tables up to 12 × 12
4	
	Year 5
5	• Divide numbers up to four digits by a one-digit number using the formal written method of short division and interpret remainders appropriately for the context
6	• Solve problems involving multiplication and division, including scaling by simple
7	fractions and problems involving simple rates
8	
	Year 6
9	• Divide numbers up to four digits by a two-digit whole number using the formal written method of long division, and interpret remainders as whole number
10	remainders, fractions or by rounding, as appropriate for the context
11	• Use their knowledge of the order of operations to carry out calculations involving the four operations
12	
13	• Use estimation to check answers and determine, in the context of a problem, an appropriate degree of accuracy
14	• *Pupils practise addition, subtraction, multiplication and division for larger numbers, using the formal written methods of columnar addition and subtraction, short and*
15	*long multiplication, and short and long division (non-statutory requirements)*
16	• Use written division methods in cases where the answer has up to two decimal places
17	Beyond Year 6 for more able extension
18	

Summary of the steps

Written Calculation: Division 2

Step 1	**Three-digit ÷ one-digit** short division revision
Step 2	**Five-digit ÷ one-digit** short division with remainders revision
Step 3	**Two-digit ÷ one-digit** long division
Step 4	**Three-digit ÷ one-digit** long division
Step 5	**Four-digit ÷ one-digit** long division
Step 6	**Four-digit ÷ one-digit** long division, answers with zeros
Check-up test 1	**Three-, four- and five-digit ÷ one-digit**
Step 7	**Three-digit ÷ 11** long division, no zeros in answers
Step 8	**Four-digit ÷ 11** long division, with zeros in answers
Step 9	**Four-digit ÷ 12** long division
Step 10	**Four-digit ÷ 13** long division
Check-up test 2	**Three- and four-digit ÷ 11, 12 or 13**
Step 11	**Four-digit ÷ 14, 15 or 16** long division
Step 12	**Four-digit ÷ 17, 18 or 19** long division, where the first two digits are smaller than the divisor
Step 13	**Four-digit ÷ a number between 11 and 19** long division
Step 14	**Four-digit ÷ a number between 11 and 19** long division, with fraction remainders
Check-up test 3	**Four-digit ÷ a number between 11 and 19, including fraction remainders**
Step 15	**Four-digit ÷ a number in the 20s** long division
Step 16	**Four-digit ÷ two-digit** long division
Step 17	**Three-digit ÷ two-digit** long division, decimal answers 1 dp
Step 18	**Three-digit ÷ two-digit** long division, decimal answers 2 dp
Final test	**Three- and four-digit ÷ two-digit, including decimal answers**

Prerequisites

Place value

- Pupils beginning this book should have already completed **Division I** and so should have an appreciation of the place value of numbers up to and beyond four-digit numbers. They should have an understanding that dividing numbers which are not multiples of the divisor results in remainders that can be given as fractions or as decimals.

Multiplication and division facts

- Pupils should also have had sufficient experience with multiplying and dividing small numbers: for example 4×8, $32 \div 4$. Pupils who know all their times tables and related division facts by heart will find learning written division much easier than those who have to work out each part of a division.

- If any pupils have not yet memorised all their tables, give them a multiplication square to provide them with the answers to the times tables. They can use these to derive the related division facts. Initially this will allow them to focus on the procedures of the written method and, as their knowledge of the facts grows, will enable them to master the written methods without the multiplication square. (A multiplication square can be downloaded for this purpose from the **Written Calculation** pages on the Schofield & Sims website.)

Teaching notes

Steps I and 2: Three- and five-digit ÷ one-digit short division with remainders revision

The first two steps revise short division to ensure pupils are ready to start this book.

- Observe whether pupils are confidently dividing using the short division method, including carrying correctly and knowing their division facts. If not, provide them with one of the assessments from **Division I** in this Teacher's Guide to see whether they need to work through all or some of the steps again.

Step 3: Two-digit ÷ one-digit long division

The long division method is first introduced here. It is vital that pupils realise that there is a repeated cycle of 'Divide, Multiply, Subtract (DMS)' in this process and that, between each round, an extra digit is brought down. Encourage them to repeat the words several times to reinforce this.

- Work through the example together, discussing each step and demonstrating the movements: for example, across to divide, up to write the answer, left to multiply by the divisor, then down to write the product and down to subtract and bring down the next digit, and so on. Remind them too that the final remainder is then written at the top with the answer.

Steps 4 and 5: Three- and four-digit ÷ one-digit long division

These steps involve repeating the process over and over for three-digit and then four-digit numbers.

- Again, continue to remind pupils of the cycle Divide, Multiply, Subtract (DMS) and bring down the next digit. Pupils should be encouraged to learn the movements of the actions.

Step 6: Four-digit ÷ one-digit long division, answers with zeros

Step 6 includes questions where, when a new digit is brought down, the number created is less than the divisor and so the answer will include a zero. Pupils often miss recording this zero, creating answers that are incorrect.

- Demonstrate the worked example and discuss the importance of writing the zero in the answer before subtracting zero and bringing down the next digit. Pupils will eventually realise that they do not need to subtract zero, but can just bring down the next digit if they prefer.

Step 7: Three-digit ÷ 11 long division, no zeros in answers

Now that pupils have had experience of the DMS cycle and have begun to get a sense of the movements involved in the method, they can begin to divide by two-digit numbers. In this step they divide by 11 as most pupils are secure in their 11 times table and so their focus can be on continuing to use the long division process. For the same reason, no zeros are included in the answers in this step.

- Encourage pupils to realise that remainders can be up to 10.

Step 8: Four-digit ÷ 11 long division, with zeros in answers

Zeros are now included and pupils divide four-digit numbers by 11.

- As for Step 6, it is vital that pupils write zeros into the answers before bringing down the next digit.

Step 9: Four-digit ÷ 12 long division

Here pupils divide by 12 as most pupils are secure in their 12 times table and so their focus can be on continuing to use the long division process. Answers may involve zeros.

- The multiples of 12 are included here, not because pupils may not know their 12 times table, but to demonstrate how having a list of the multiples before beginning the long division process can speed up the actual working. In later steps pupils are encouraged to do this for themselves.

- Encourage pupils to realise that remainders can be up to 11.

Step 10: Four-digit ÷ 13 long division

The process is continued for dividing by 13 and a list of multiples of 13 is provided.

Step 11: Four-digit ÷ 14, 15 or 16 long division

Here the divisors include 14, 15 and 16. Some of the multiples are provided but pupils are encouraged to write the missing values.

- Discuss how patterns of numbers in the multiples can be used to help find the missing multiples: for example, adding 14 to the previous multiple, doubling 4 times to find 8 times, subtracting from the following multiple. Ultimately, pupils should be able to write their own list of multiples quite quickly using a range of appropriate strategies.

Step 12: Four-digit ÷ 17, 18 or 19 long division, where the first two digits are smaller than the divisor

This step involves looking at the first three digits together, rather than the first two.

- Observe which pupils are working confidently and accurately.

Step 13: Four-digit ÷ a number between 11 and 19 long division

This step extends pupils to dividing by teens numbers, and writing their own sets of multiples as a means of working more easily on the process of long division.

- More confident learners perhaps do not need to write all the multiples, but it is suggested that less confident learners complete all of them before beginning the calculation.

Step 14: Four-digit ÷ a number between 11 and 19 long division, with fraction remainders

This step extends more able pupils by showing them that remainders can be written as fractions.

- Pupils should be confident in understanding fractions and realise that, if the whole number remainder is divided by the divisor, then the denominator of the fraction will be the divisor with the numerator being the remainder. Fractions may be simplified, where possible, but this is not the focus here.

Steps 15 and 16: Four-digit ÷ two-digit long division

These steps continue the method of long division by other two-digit numbers. Step 15 involves numbers in the 20s and Step 16 involves other two-digit numbers.

Steps 17 and 18: Three-digit ÷ two-digit long division, decimal answers

These final two steps show how decimal answers can be found. These challenge even the most able Key Stage 2 pupils. The written form of subtraction is also shown to demonstrate how this can be used when working out long divisions.

- Ensure that pupils are familiar with the column headings for tenths, hundredths and thousandths.
- Explain that the decimal point in the answer must be aligned with the one in the question.

Assessment test 1 and **Assessment test 2** at the back of this book will help you to identify the steps that each pupil has mastered, as each question number in the tests corresponds to a step.

Further practice questions for each step are given in the Teacher's Resource Book. Photocopy and cut out each section if required.

Problem solving questions, that is mixed division word problems for the steps, are provided in the Teacher's Resource Book.

Assessment resources

Assessment test 1

Name: _____

Class/Set: _____ Date: _____

**Using squared paper for working, work out your answer to each question.
Then write your answer on the line next to the question.**

1 36 + 42 _____ ☐ 1

2 358 + 231 _____ ☐ 2

3 514 + 257 _____ ☐ 3

4 671 + 235 _____ ☐ 4

5 588 + 551 _____ ☐ 5

6 613 + 427 + 235 _____ ☐ 6

7 4537 + 2632 _____ ☐ 7

8 878 + 787 _____ ☐ 8

9 3956 + 4937 _____ ☐ 9

10 8359 + 5281 _____ ☐ 10

11 5756 + 7866 _____ ☐ 11

12 3686 + 875 + 6542 _____ ☐ 12

13 75 678 + 26 369 _____ ☐ 13

14 57 546 + 548 + 5733 + 2553 _____ ☐ 14

15 364 518 + 231 465 _____ ☐ 15

16 354.7 + 63.6 _____ ☐ 16

17 463.68 + 77.71 _____ ☐ 17

18 46.875 + 25.7 _____ ☐ 18

Total test score

☐ 18

Score	1	2	3	4	5	6	7	8	9	10	11	12	13	14	15	16	17	18
%	6	11	17	22	28	33	39	44	50	56	61	67	72	78	83	89	94	100

Assessment test 2

Name: _____

Class/Set: _____   Date: _____

**Using squared paper for working, work out your answer to each question.
Then write your answer on the line next to the question.**

1 53 + 44 _____ ☐ 1

2 247 + 342 _____ ☐ 2

3 428 + 329 _____ ☐ 3

4 684 + 281 _____ ☐ 4

5 735 + 728 _____ ☐ 5

6 426 + 229 + 318 _____ ☐ 6

7 4836 + 1531 _____ ☐ 7

8 786 + 568 _____ ☐ 8

9 5316 + 3935 _____ ☐ 9

10 9359 + 2285 _____ ☐ 10

11 8667 + 4865 _____ ☐ 11

12 5785 + 254 + 6836 _____ ☐ 12

13 55 443 + 37 368 _____ ☐ 13

14 36 506 + 948 + 24 534 + 6443 _____ ☐ 14

15 795 518 + 264 433 _____ ☐ 15

16 474.8 + 83.7 _____ ☐ 16

17 574.68 + 85.73 _____ ☐ 17

18 44.933 + 5.74 _____ ☐ 18

Total test score

☐ 18

Score	1	2	3	4	5	6	7	8	9	10	11	12	13	14	15	16	17	18
%	6	11	17	22	28	33	39	44	50	56	61	67	72	78	83	89	94	100

From: **Written Calculation: Teacher's Guide** by Hilary Koll and Steve Mills (ISBN 978 07217 1278 9). Copyright © Schofield & Sims Ltd, 2015. Published by Schofield & Sims Ltd, Dogley Mill, Fenay Bridge, Huddersfield HD8 0NQ, UK (www.schofieldandsims.co.uk). This page may be photocopied after purchase for use within your school or institution only.

Assessment test 1

Name: _____

Class/Set: _____   Date: _____

**Using squared paper for working, work out your answer to each question.
Then write your answer on the line next to the question.**

1 72 – 41 _____ ☐ 1

2 657 – 321 _____ ☐ 2

3 442 – 326 _____ ☐ 3

4 777 – 392 _____ ☐ 4

5 618 – 432 _____ ☐ 5

6 7216 – 4813 _____ ☐ 6

7 7666 – 5717 _____ ☐ 7

8 652 – 288 _____ ☐ 8

9 4218 – 2583 _____ ☐ 9

10 3508 – 2359 _____ ☐ 10

11 42 982 – 27 224 _____ ☐ 11

12 69 628 – 42 872 _____ ☐ 12

13 87 604 – 42 487 _____ ☐ 13

14 78 222 – 24 688 _____ ☐ 14

15 92 007 – 38 749 _____ ☐ 15

16 603 325 – 478 437 _____ ☐ 16

17 35.86 – 23.19 _____ ☐ 17

18 63.58 – 2.531 _____ ☐ 18

Total test score

Score	1	2	3	4	5	6	7	8	9	10	11	12	13	14	15	16	17	18
%	6	11	17	22	28	33	39	44	50	56	61	67	72	78	83	89	94	100

☐ 18

Assessment test 2

Name: _____

Class/Set: _____   Date: _____

**Using squared paper for working, work out your answer to each question.
Then write your answer on the line next to the question.**

1 86 – 53 _____ ☐ 1

2 794 – 531 _____ ☐ 2

3 441 – 328 _____ ☐ 3

4 737 – 492 _____ ☐ 4

5 671 – 462 _____ ☐ 5

6 8417 – 4713 _____ ☐ 6

7 8636 – 5718 _____ ☐ 7

8 637 – 269 _____ ☐ 8

9 4458 – 2673 _____ ☐ 9

10 8508 – 2369 _____ ☐ 10

11 41 984 – 27 516 _____ ☐ 11

12 68 628 – 42 872 _____ ☐ 12

13 88 603 – 52 385 _____ ☐ 13

14 89 221 – 24 766 _____ ☐ 14

15 72 007 – 38 758 _____ ☐ 15

16 634 325 – 376 837 _____ ☐ 16

17 435.24 – 57.39 _____ ☐ 17

18 88.8 – 2.754 _____ ☐ 18

Total test score

☐ 18

Score	1	2	3	4	5	6	7	8	9	10	11	12	13	14	15	16	17	18
%	6	11	17	22	28	33	39	44	50	56	61	67	72	78	83	89	94	100

Assessment test 1

Name: _____

Class/Set: _____ Date: _____

**Using squared paper for working, work out your answer to each question.
Then write your answer on the line next to the question.**

1 23 × 3 _____ ☐ 1

2 26 × 3 _____ ☐ 2

3 14 × 6 _____ ☐ 3

4 125 × 3 _____ ☐ 4

5 181 × 5 _____ ☐ 5

6 72 × 4 _____ ☐ 6

7 76 × 8 _____ ☐ 7

8 143 × 6 _____ ☐ 8

9 413 × 7 _____ ☐ 9

10 138 × 7 _____ ☐ 10

11 1241 × 6 _____ ☐ 11

12 6968 × 4 _____ ☐ 12

13 87 604 × 7 _____ ☐ 13

14 782 223 × 8 _____ ☐ 14

15 927 × 20 _____ ☐ 15

16 625 × 60 _____ ☐ 16

17 3586 × 70 _____ ☐ 17

18 6247 × 400 _____ ☐ 18

Total test score   ☐ 18

Score	1	2	3	4	5	6	7	8	9	10	11	12	13	14	15	16	17	18
%	6	11	17	22	28	33	39	44	50	56	61	67	72	78	83	89	94	100

From: **Written Calculation: Teacher's Guide** by Hilary Koll and Steve Mills (ISBN 978 07217 1278 9). Copyright © Schofield & Sims Ltd, 2015. Published by Schofield & Sims Ltd, Dogley Mill, Fenay Bridge, Huddersfield HD8 0NQ, UK (www.schofieldandsims.co.uk). This page may be photocopied after purchase for use within your school or institution only.

Assessment test 2

Name: _____

Class/Set: _____   Date: _____

**Using squared paper for working, work out your answer to each question.
Then write your answer on the line next to the question.**

1 21×4 _____ ☐ 1

2 16×5 _____ ☐ 2

3 13×7 _____ ☐ 3

4 223×4 _____ ☐ 4

5 171×4 _____ ☐ 5

6 81×6 _____ ☐ 6

7 86×8 _____ ☐ 7

8 153×6 _____ ☐ 8

9 418×4 _____ ☐ 9

10 137×6 _____ ☐ 10

11 2762×3 _____ ☐ 11

12 6862×7 _____ ☐ 12

13 $88\,603 \times 5$ _____ ☐ 13

14 $8\,920\,221 \times 4$ _____ ☐ 14

15 723×20 _____ ☐ 15

16 574×90 _____ ☐ 16

17 4353×80 _____ ☐ 17

18 438×6000 _____ ☐ 18

Total test score ☐ 18

Score	1	2	3	4	5	6	7	8	9	10	11	12	13	14	15	16	17	18
%	6	11	17	22	28	33	39	44	50	56	61	67	72	78	83	89	94	100

Assessment test 1

Name: _____

Class/Set: _____   Date: _____

**Using squared paper for working, work out your answer to each question.
Then write your answer on the line next to the question.**

1   653 × 7   _____ ☐ 1

2   236 × 20   _____ ☐ 2

3   124 × 12   _____ ☐ 3

4   525 × 13   _____ ☐ 4

5   981 × 15   _____ ☐ 5

6   723 × 40   _____ ☐ 6

7   36 × 22   _____ ☐ 7

8   152 × 56   _____ ☐ 8

9   455 × 79   _____ ☐ 9

10   1368 × 85   _____ ☐ 10

11   124 × 600   _____ ☐ 11

12   696 × 430   _____ ☐ 12

13   253 × 124   _____ ☐ 13

14   788 × 678   _____ ☐ 14

15   47 × 0.4   _____ ☐ 15

16   6.5 × 63   _____ ☐ 16

17   3.6 × 7.2   _____ ☐ 17

18   6.27 × 4.2   _____ ☐ 18

Total test score   ☐ 18

Score	1	2	3	4	5	6	7	8	9	10	11	12	13	14	15	16	17	18
%	6	11	17	22	28	33	39	44	50	56	61	67	72	78	83	89	94	100

Assessment test 2

Name: _____

Class/Set: _____   Date: _____

**Using squared paper for working, work out your answer to each question.
Then write your answer on the line next to the question.**

1 235×5 _____ ☐ 1

2 146×20 _____ ☐ 2

3 202×17 _____ ☐ 3

4 242×14 _____ ☐ 4

5 783×14 _____ ☐ 5

6 871×60 _____ ☐ 6

7 281×34 _____ ☐ 7

8 153×65 _____ ☐ 8

9 718×47 _____ ☐ 9

10 $13\,754 \times 67$ _____ ☐ 10

11 276×300 _____ ☐ 11

12 686×720 _____ ☐ 12

13 223×553 _____ ☐ 13

14 896×487 _____ ☐ 14

15 7.3×5 _____ ☐ 15

16 57×9.3 _____ ☐ 16

17 4.3×8.1 _____ ☐ 17

18 43.8×6.2 _____ ☐ 18

Total test score ☐ 18

Score	1	2	3	4	5	6	7	8	9	10	11	12	13	14	15	16	17	18
%	6	11	17	22	28	33	39	44	50	56	61	67	72	78	83	89	94	100

From: **Written Calculation: Teacher's Guide** by Hilary Koll and Steve Mills (ISBN 978 07217 1278 9). Copyright © Schofield & Sims Ltd, 2015. Published by Schofield & Sims Ltd, Dogley Mill, Fenay Bridge, Huddersfield HD8 0NQ, UK (www.schofieldandsims.co.uk). This page may be photocopied after purchase for use within your school or institution only.

Assessment test 1

Name: _____

Class/Set: _____   Date: _____

**Using squared paper for working, work out your answer to each question.
Then write your answer on the line next to the question.**

1	$39 \div 3$	_____	☐ 1
2	$848 \div 4$	_____	☐ 2
3	$78 \div 6$	_____	☐ 3
4	$60 \div 4$	_____	☐ 4
5	$576 \div 3$	_____	☐ 5
6	$368 \div 4$	_____	☐ 6
7	$872 \div 4$	_____	☐ 7
8	$848 \div 8$	_____	☐ 8
9	$8852 \div 4$	_____	☐ 9
10	$456 \div 8$	_____	☐ 10
11	$6874 \div 7$	_____	☐ 11
12	$7773 \div 4$ — Give your answer with a remainder.	_____	☐ 12
13	$87604 \div 7$ — Give your answer with a remainder.	_____	☐ 13
14	$2223 \div 8$ — Give the remainder as a fraction.	_____	☐ 14
15	$9237 \div 6$ — Give the remainder as a decimal.	_____	☐ 15
16	$9161 \div 4$ — Give the remainder as a decimal.	_____	☐ 16
17	$911 \div 3$ — Give the remainder as a recurring decimal.	_____	☐ 17
18	$6.47 \div 4$	_____	☐ 18

Total test score ☐ 18

Score	1	2	3	4	5	6	7	8	9	10	11	12	13	14	15	16	17	18
%	6	11	17	22	28	33	39	44	50	56	61	67	72	78	83	89	94	100

From: **Written Calculation: Teacher's Guide** by Hilary Koll and Steve Mills (ISBN 978 07217 1278 9). Copyright © Schofield & Sims Ltd, 2015. Published by Schofield & Sims Ltd, Dogley Mill, Fenay Bridge, Huddersfield HD8 0NQ, UK (www.schofieldandsims.co.uk). This page may be photocopied after purchase for use within your school or institution only.

Assessment test 2

Name: _____

Class/Set: _____ Date: _____

**Using squared paper for working, work out your answer to each question.
Then write your answer on the line next to the question.**

1 93 ÷ 3 _____ ☐ 1

2 484 ÷ 4 _____ ☐ 2

3 56 ÷ 4 _____ ☐ 3

4 68 ÷ 4 _____ ☐ 4

5 855 ÷ 5 _____ ☐ 5

6 244 ÷ 4 _____ ☐ 6

7 464 ÷ 4 _____ ☐ 7

8 612 ÷ 6 _____ ☐ 8

9 9246 ÷ 3 _____ ☐ 9

10 288 ÷ 6 _____ ☐ 10

11 9144 ÷ 6 _____ ☐ 11

12 6965 ÷ 8   Give your answer with a remainder. _____ ☐ 12

13 47 364 ÷ 6 _____ ☐ 13

14 7822 ÷ 8   Give the remainder as a fraction. _____ ☐ 14

15 7427 ÷ 2   Give the remainder as a decimal. _____ ☐ 15

16 1806 ÷ 8   Give the remainder as a decimal. _____ ☐ 16

17 353 ÷ 9   Give the remainder as a recurring decimal. _____ ☐ 17

18 6.46 ÷ 8 _____ ☐ 18

Total test score ☐ 18

Score	1	2	3	4	5	6	7	8	9	10	11	12	13	14	15	16	17	18
%	6	11	17	22	28	33	39	44	50	56	61	67	72	78	83	89	94	100

From: **Written Calculation: Teacher's Guide** by Hilary Koll and Steve Mills (ISBN 978 07217 1278 9). Copyright © Schofield & Sims Ltd, 2015. Published by Schofield & Sims Ltd, Dogley Mill, Fenay Bridge, Huddersfield HD8 0NQ, UK (www.schofieldandsims.co.uk). This page may be photocopied after purchase for use within your school or institution only.

Assessment test 1

Name: _____

Class/Set: _____   Date: _____

**Using squared paper for working, work out your answer to each question.
Then write your answer on the line next to the question.**
Give your answers with remainders, unless told otherwise.

1 $942 \div 3$ _____ ☐ 1

2 $48474 \div 5$ _____ ☐ 2

3 $98 \div 6$ _____ ☐ 3

4 $654 \div 4$ _____ ☐ 4

5 $5754 \div 3$ _____ ☐ 5

6 $2408 \div 4$ _____ ☐ 6

7 $872 \div 11$ _____ ☐ 7

8 $8848 \div 11$ _____ ☐ 8

9 $6852 \div 12$ _____ ☐ 9

10 $4564 \div 13$ _____ ☐ 10

11 $6874 \div 14$ _____ ☐ 11

12 $1773 \div 18$ _____ ☐ 12

13 $8764 \div 13$ _____ ☐ 13

14 $7822 \div 18$ Give the remainder as a fraction. _____ ☐ 14

15 $9237 \div 26$ Give the remainder as a fraction. _____ ☐ 15

16 $9161 \div 44$ Give the remainder as a fraction. _____ ☐ 16

17 $567 \div 35$ Give the remainder as a decimal. _____ ☐ 17

18 $469 \div 28$ Give the remainder as a decimal. _____ ☐ 18

Total test score   ☐

Score	1	2	3	4	5	6	7	8	9	10	11	12	13	14	15	16	17	18
%	6	11	17	22	28	33	39	44	50	56	61	67	72	78	83	89	94	100

18

From: **Written Calculation: Teacher's Guide** by Hilary Koll and Steve Mills (ISBN 978 07217 1278 9). Copyright © Schofield & Sims Ltd, 2015. Published by Schofield & Sims Ltd, Dogley Mill, Fenay Bridge, Huddersfield HD8 0NQ, UK (www.schofieldandsims.co.uk). This page may be photocopied after purchase for use within your school or institution only.

Assessment test 2

Name: _____

Class/Set: _____ Date: _____

Using squared paper for working, work out your answer to each question.
Then write your answer on the line next to the question.
Give your answers with remainders, unless told otherwise.

1 933 ÷ 3 _____ ☐ 1

2 4843 ÷ 4 _____ ☐ 2

3 98 ÷ 4 _____ ☐ 3

4 574 ÷ 3 _____ ☐ 4

5 8585 ÷ 5 _____ ☐ 5

6 4228 ÷ 7 _____ ☐ 6

7 464 ÷ 11 _____ ☐ 7

8 6702 ÷ 11 _____ ☐ 8

9 9246 ÷ 12 _____ ☐ 9

10 6288 ÷ 13 _____ ☐ 10

11 9144 ÷ 15 _____ ☐ 11

12 1265 ÷ 17 _____ ☐ 12

13 4736 ÷ 19 _____ ☐ 13

14 7822 ÷ 18   Give the remainder as a fraction. _____ ☐ 14

15 7427 ÷ 24   Give the remainder as a fraction. _____ ☐ 15

16 1806 ÷ 28   Give the remainder as a fraction. _____ ☐ 16

17 882 ÷ 36   Give the remainder as a decimal. _____ ☐ 17

18 552 ÷ 32   Give the remainder as a decimal. _____ ☐ 18

Total test score

☐ 18

Score	1	2	3	4	5	6	7	8	9	10	11	12	13	14	15	16	17	18
%	6	11	17	22	28	33	39	44	50	56	61	67	72	78	83	89	94	100

From: **Written Calculation: Teacher's Guide** by Hilary Koll and Steve Mills (ISBN 978 07217 1278 9). Copyright © Schofield & Sims Ltd, 2015. Published by Schofield & Sims Ltd, Dogley Mill, Fenay Bridge, Huddersfield HD8 0NQ, UK (www.schofieldandsims.co.uk). This page may be photocopied after purchase for use within your school or institution only.

Mixed calculations test

Name: _____

Class/Set: _____ Date: _____

**Using squared paper for working, work out your answer to each question.
Then write your answer on the line next to the question.**

1 The price of a computer that cost £1257 is increased by £186. What is the new price? _____ □ 1

2 There were 738 people in a cinema. 368 were children. How many were adults? _____ □ 2

3 A shop has 13 bags each containing six bananas. How many bananas is that altogether? _____ □ 3

4 There are 2846 rooms in a big hotel. If 1856 of the rooms were taken, how many rooms were empty? _____ □ 4

5 There are 246 seats in a train carriage. How many people can sit in four carriages? _____ □ 5

6 A box holds 116 paperclips. How many paper clips are there in four boxes? _____ □ 6

7 Al scored 8954 points in the first round of a computer game and 5897 in the second round. What was his total score? _____ □ 7

8 Find the product of 137 and 7. _____ □ 8

9 At a rugby match there were 738 away fans, and three times as many home fans. How many home fans were there? _____ □ 9

10 Ruby had £9443. She spent £6741 of it on a new car. How much has she now? _____ □ 10

11 Which year is 724 years after 1247 AD? _____ □ 11

12 Divide 366 equally by 3. _____ □ 12

13 There are 968 cows equally grouped in eight herds. How many cows are in each herd? _____ □ 13

14 Find the sum of 474, 254 and 697. _____ □ 14

15 If I earn £41 103 a year, how much is that each month? _____ □ 15

Total test score

Score	1	2	3	4	5	6	7	8	9	10	11	12	13	14	15
%	7	13	20	27	33	40	47	53	60	67	73	80	87	93	100

□ 15

From: **Written Calculation: Teacher's Guide** by Hilary Koll and Steve Mills (ISBN 978 07217 1278 9). Copyright © Schofield & Sims Ltd, 2015. Published by Schofield & Sims Ltd, Dogley Mill, Fenay Bridge, Huddersfield HD8 0NQ, UK (www.schofieldandsims.co.uk).

Assessment test answers

Addition

Assessment test 1 answers

1	78	**10**	13 640
2	589	**11**	13 622
3	771	**12**	11 103
4	906	**13**	102 047
5	1139	**14**	66 380
6	1275	**15**	595 983
7	7169	**16**	418.3
8	1665	**17**	541.39
9	8893	**18**	72.575

Assessment test 2 answers

1	97	**10**	11 644
2	589	**11**	13 532
3	757	**12**	12 875
4	965	**13**	92 811
5	1463	**14**	68 431
6	973	**15**	1 059 951
7	6367	**16**	558.5
8	1354	**17**	660.41
9	9251	**18**	50.673

Subtraction

Assessment test 1 answers

1	31	**10**	1149
2	336	**11**	15 758
3	116	**12**	26 756
4	385	**13**	45 117
5	186	**14**	53 534
6	2403	**15**	53 258
7	1949	**16**	124 888
8	364	**17**	12.67
9	1635	**18**	61.049

Assessment test 2 answers

1	33	**10**	6139
2	263	**11**	14 468
3	113	**12**	25 756
4	245	**13**	36 218
5	209	**14**	64 455
6	3704	**15**	33 249
7	2918	**16**	257 488
8	368	**17**	377.85
9	1785	**18**	86.046

Assessment test answers

Multiplication 1

Assessment test 1 answers

1	69	**10**	966
2	78	**11**	7446
3	84	**12**	27872
4	375	**13**	613228
5	905	**14**	6257784
6	288	**15**	18540
7	608	**16**	37500
8	858	**17**	251020
9	2891	**18**	2498800

Assessment test 2 answers

1	84	**10**	822
2	80	**11**	8286
3	91	**12**	48034
4	892	**13**	443015
5	684	**14**	35680884
6	486	**15**	14460
7	688	**16**	51660
8	918	**17**	348240
9	1672	**18**	2628000

Multiplication 2

Assessment test 1 answers

1	4571	**10**	116280
2	4720	**11**	74400
3	1488	**12**	299280
4	6825	**13**	31372
5	14715	**14**	534264
6	28920	**15**	18.8
7	792	**16**	409.5
8	8512	**17**	25.92
9	35945	**18**	26.334

Assessment test 2 answers

1	1175	**10**	921518
2	2920	**11**	82800
3	3434	**12**	493920
4	3388	**13**	123319
5	10962	**14**	436352
6	52260	**15**	36.5
7	9554	**16**	530.1
8	9945	**17**	34.83
9	33746	**18**	271.56

Assessment test answers

Division 1

Assessment test 1 answers

1 13	**10** 57
2 212	**11** 982
3 13	**12** 1943 r1
4 15	**13** 12 514 r6
5 192	**14** $277\frac{7}{8}$
6 92	**15** 1539.5
7 218	**16** 2290.25
8 106	**17** $303.\dot{6}$
9 2213	**18** 1.6175

Assessment test 2 answers

1 31	**10** 48
2 121	**11** 1524
3 14	**12** 870 r5
4 17	**13** 7894
5 171	**14** $977\frac{6}{8}$
6 61	**15** 3713.5
7 116	**16** 225.75
8 102	**17** $39.\dot{2}$
9 3082	**18** 0.8075

Division 2

Assessment test 1 answers

1 314	**10** 351 r1
2 9694 r4	**11** 491
3 16 r2	**12** 98 r9
4 163 r2	**13** 674 r2
5 1918	**14** $434\frac{5}{9}$ (or $\frac{10}{18}$)
6 602	**15** $355\frac{7}{26}$
7 79 r3	**16** $208\frac{9}{44}$
8 804 r4	**17** 16.2
9 571	**18** 16.75

Assessment test 2 answers

1 311	**10** 483 r9
2 1210 r3	**11** 609 r9
3 24 r2	**12** 74 r7
4 191 r1	**13** 249 r5
5 1717	**14** $434\frac{5}{9}$ (or $\frac{10}{18}$)
6 604	**15** $309\frac{11}{24}$
7 42 r2	**16** $64\frac{14}{28}$ (or $\frac{1}{2}$)
8 609 r3	**17** 24.5
9 770 r6	**18** 17.25

Mixed calculations test answers

Mixed calculations

Answers

1 £1443

2 370

3 78

4 990

5 984

6 464

7 14851

8 959

9 2214

10 £2702

11 1971 (AD)

12 122

13 121

14 1425

15 £3425.25